Easy Listening

Music arranged and processed by Barnes Music Engraving Ltd, East Sussex TN22 4HA, England
Cover design by xheight Limited
Published 1996

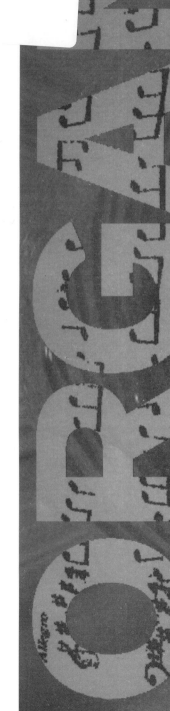

ALWAYS ON MY MIND

Words and Music by WAYNE THOMPSON, MARK JAMES and JOHNNY CHRISTOPHER

Registration
Upper: Pop Organ or Brass
Lower: Organ / Strings
Pedal: 8' Electric Bass
Rhythm Disco (8 Beat)
Tempo ♩ = 120

4

CHANSON D'AMOUR

Words and Music by WAYNE SHANKLIN

Registration
Upper: Accordion or Harmonica
Lower: Brass / Piano
Pedal: 8' Acoustic Bass
Rhythm Swing or Bounce
Tempo ♩ = 112

EARTH ANGEL (Will You Be Mine)

Words and Music by CURTIS EDWARD WILLIAMS, GAYNEL HODGE and JESSE L BELVIN

Registration
Upper: 16' Piano / Oohs or Vibraphone / Oohs
Lower: Piano / Strings
Pedal: 8' Acoustic Bass
Rhythm Swing or Bounce
Tempo ♩. = 82

EVERYBODY'S TALKIN'

Words and Music by FRED NEIL

Registration
Upper: Harmonica / Strings
Lower: Strings / Electric Piano
Pedal: 8' Acoustic Bass
Rhythm   8 Beat
Tempo   ♩ = 116

GOODBYE GIRL

Words and Music by DAVID GATES

Registration
Upper: Guitar with Leslie Vibrato
Lower: Strings / Piano
Pedal: 8' Acoustic Bass
Rhythm 16 Beat
Tempo ♩ = 80

All your life you've wait-ed for love to come and stay. And now that I have found you, you must not slip a-way. I know it's hard be-liev-ing the words

I know you've been tak-en a-fraid to hurt a-gain. You fight the love you feel for me in-stead of giv-ing in. But I can wait for-ev-er for help-

IT'S ALL IN THE GAME

Words by CARL SIGMAN
Music by CHARLES G DAWES

Registration
Upper: Pop Organ
Lower: Piano / Strings
Pedal: 8' Acoustic Bass
Rhythm Shuffle or Slow Rock 12/8
Tempo ♩ = 82

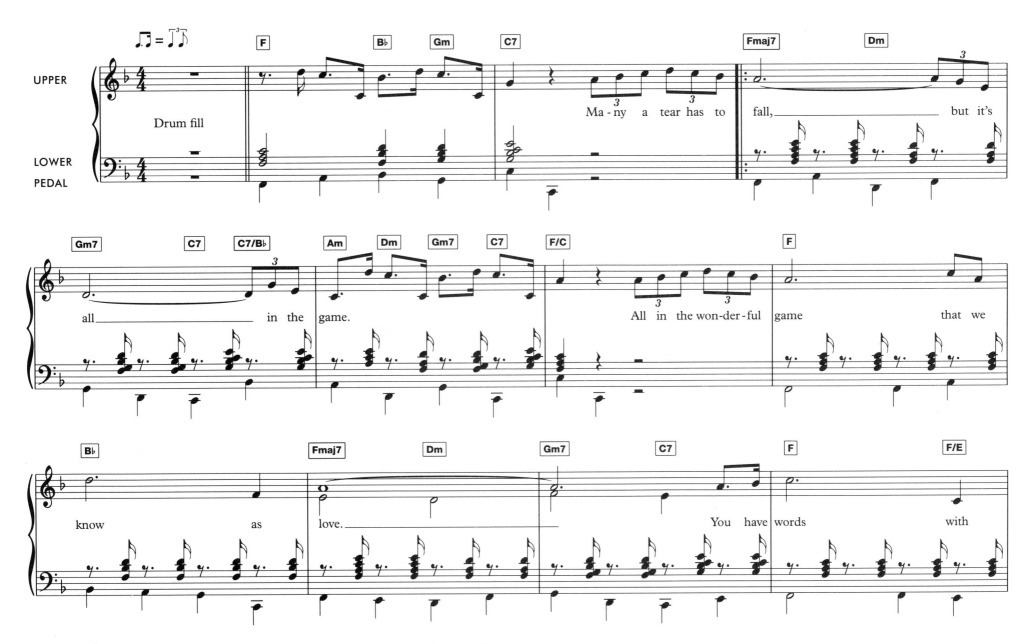

IF I WERE A CARPENTER

Words and Music by TIM HARDIN

Registration
Upper: Glockenspiel / Vibraphone or Organ
Lower: Strings / Electric Piano
Pedal: 8' Electric Bass
Rhythm   8 Beat
Tempo   ♩ = 114

LAUGHTER IN THE RAIN

Words and Music by NEIL SEDAKA and PHIL CODY

Registration
Upper: Organ / Strings
Lower: Piano / Strings
Pedal: 8' Acoustic Bass
Rhythm   8 Beat
Tempo   ♩ = 118

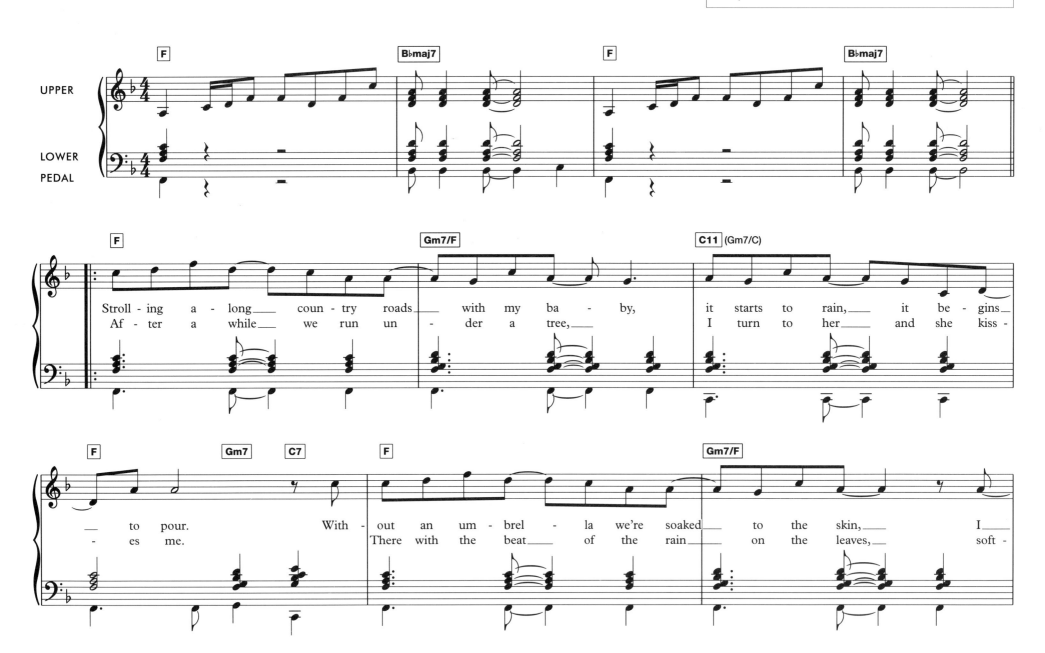

Strolling a-long country roads with my ba-by, it starts to rain, it be-gins to pour. With-out an um-brel-la we're soaked to the skin, I

Af-ter a while we run un-der a tree, I turn to her and she kiss-es me. There with the beat of the rain on the leaves, soft-

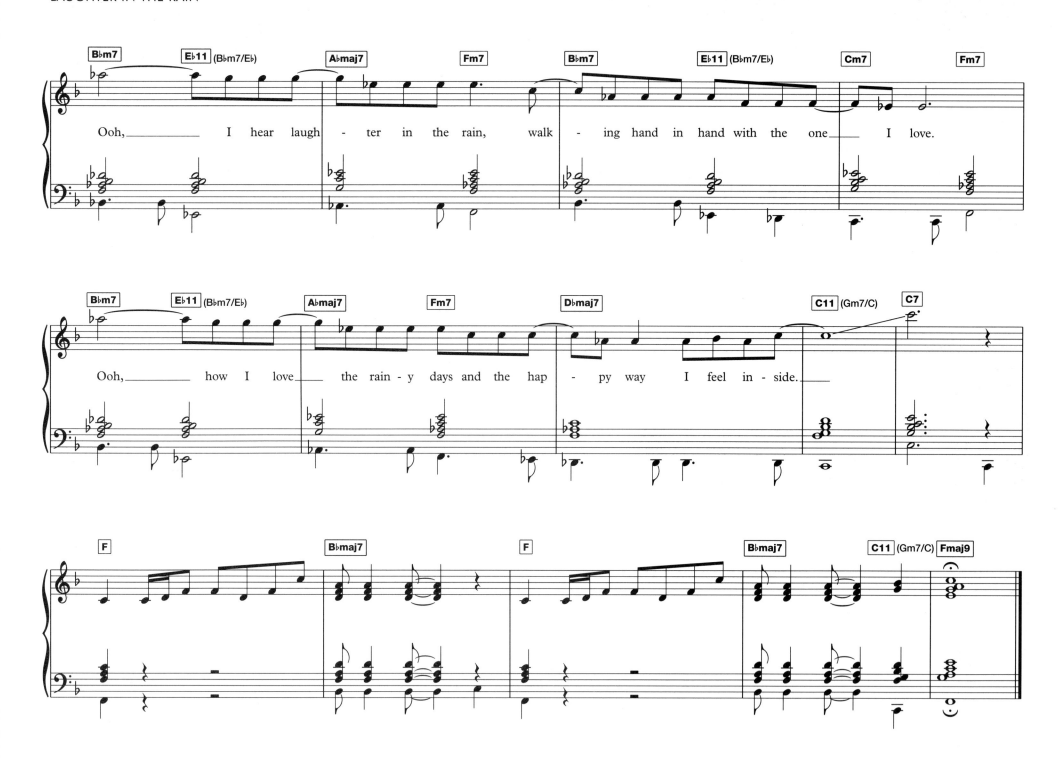

MOONLIGHTING

Words by AL JARREAU
Music by LEE HOLDRIDGE

Registration
Upper: Synth. Brass or Electric Guitar
Lower: Brass / Strings
Pedal: 8' Electric Bass
Rhythm 8 Beat or Funk
Tempo ♩ = 100

NOW AND FOREVER

Words and Music by RICHARD MARX

Registration
Upper: Flute / Strings
Lower: Strings / Acoustic Guitar
Pedal: 8' Acoustic Bass
Rhythm 8 Beat
Tempo ♩ = 80

When-ev-er I'm wear-y from the bat-tles that rage in my head,
Some-times I just hold you, too caught up in me to see

you make sense of a mad-ness when my sa-ni-ty hangs by a thread.
I'm hold-ing a for-tune that hea-ven has giv-en to me.

TRAINS AND BOATS AND PLANES

Words by HAL DAVID
Music by BURT BACHARACH

Registration
Upper: Mellow Brass or Pop Organ
Lower: Piano / Brass
Pedal: 8' Electric Bass
Rhythm Bossa Nova
Tempo ♩ = 112

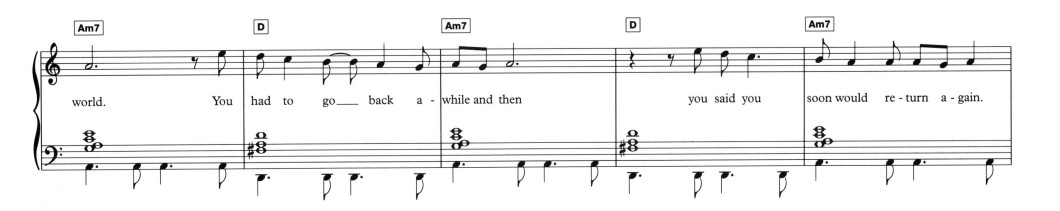

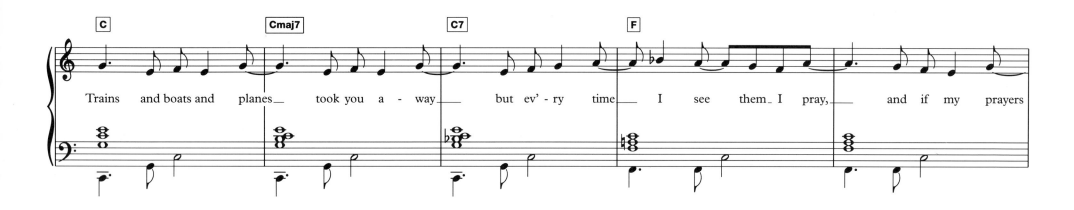

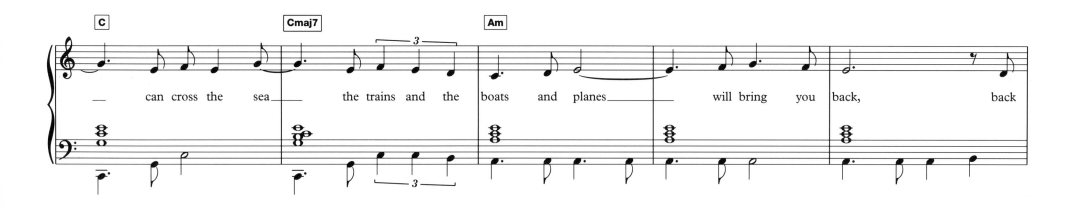

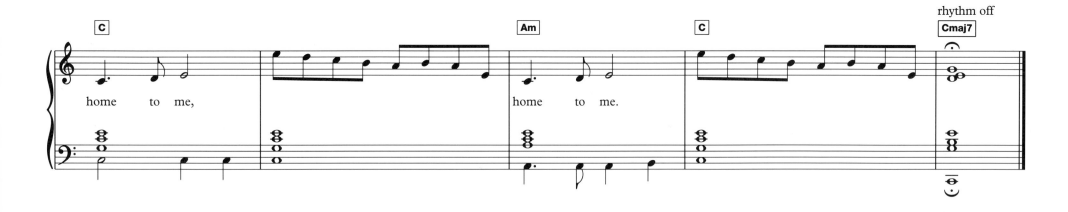

THE ROSE

Words and Music by AMANDA McBROOM

Registration
Upper: Piano / 12 String Guitar
Lower: Strings / Acoustic Guitar
Pedal: 8' Acoustic Bass
Rhythm 8 Beat
Tempo ♩ = 66

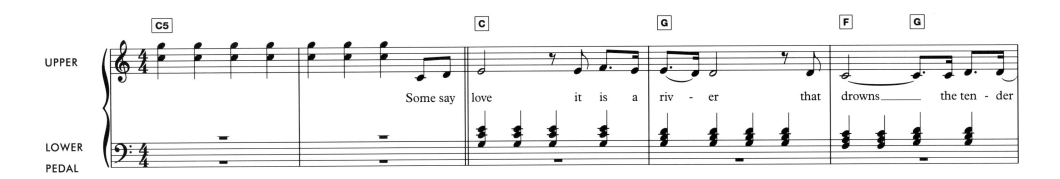

Some say love it is a riv-er that drowns____ the ten-der

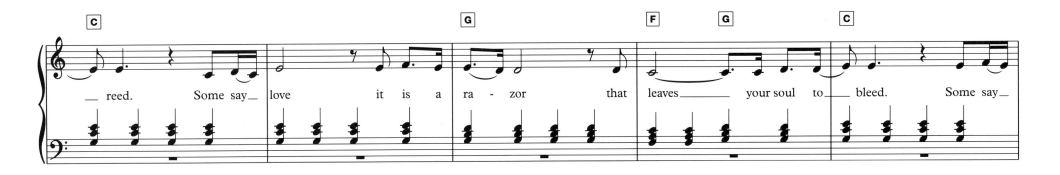

__ reed. Some say__ love it is a ra-zor that leaves____ your soul to__ bleed. Some say__

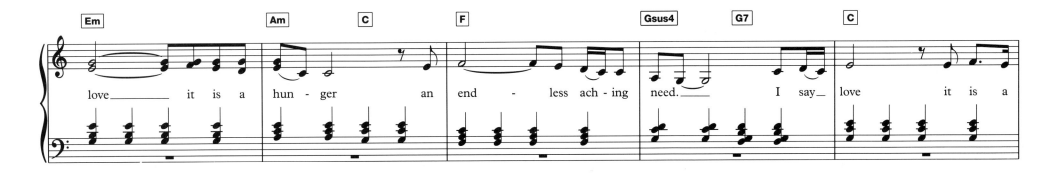

love____ it is a hun-ger an end-less ach-ing need.____ I say__ love it is a

WE DON'T CRY OUT LOUD

Words and Music by CAROLE BAYER SAGER and PETER ALLEN

Registration
Upper: Pop Organ. Add Fast Leslie (tremulant)
Lower: Organ / Strings
Pedal: 8' Electric Bass
Rhythm   16 Beat
Tempo   ♩ = 62

WHY DO FOOLS FALL IN LOVE?

Words and Music by FRANKIE LYMON and GEORGE GOLDNER

Registration
Upper: Electric Guitar / Organ or Brass
Lower: Brass / Piano
Pedal: 8' Electric Bass
Rhythm Pop Rock or Bounce
Tempo ♩ = 180

YOU MAKE ME FEEL BRAND NEW

Words and Music by THOMAS BELL and LINDA CREED

Registration
Upper: Strings / Synth. or Pop Organ
Lower: Strings / Electric Piano
Pedal: 8' Electric Bass
Rhythm (Verse) 8 Beat (Chorus) 16 Beat
Tempo ♩ = 80

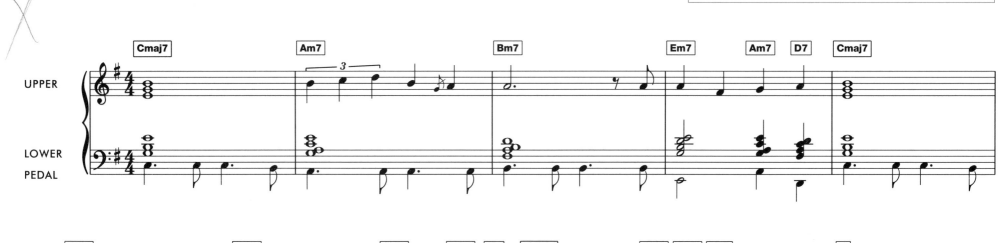

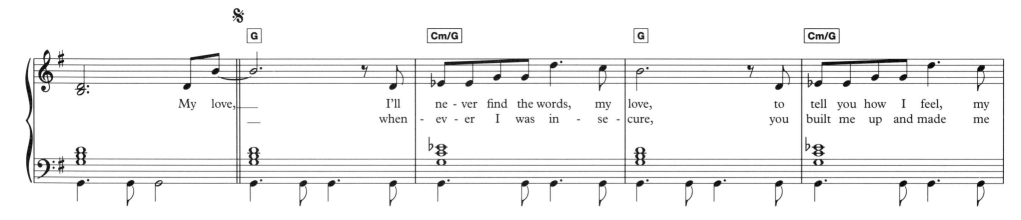

My love, ___ I'll ne-ver find the words, my love, to tell you how I feel, my
when-ev-er I was in-se-cure, you built me up and made me

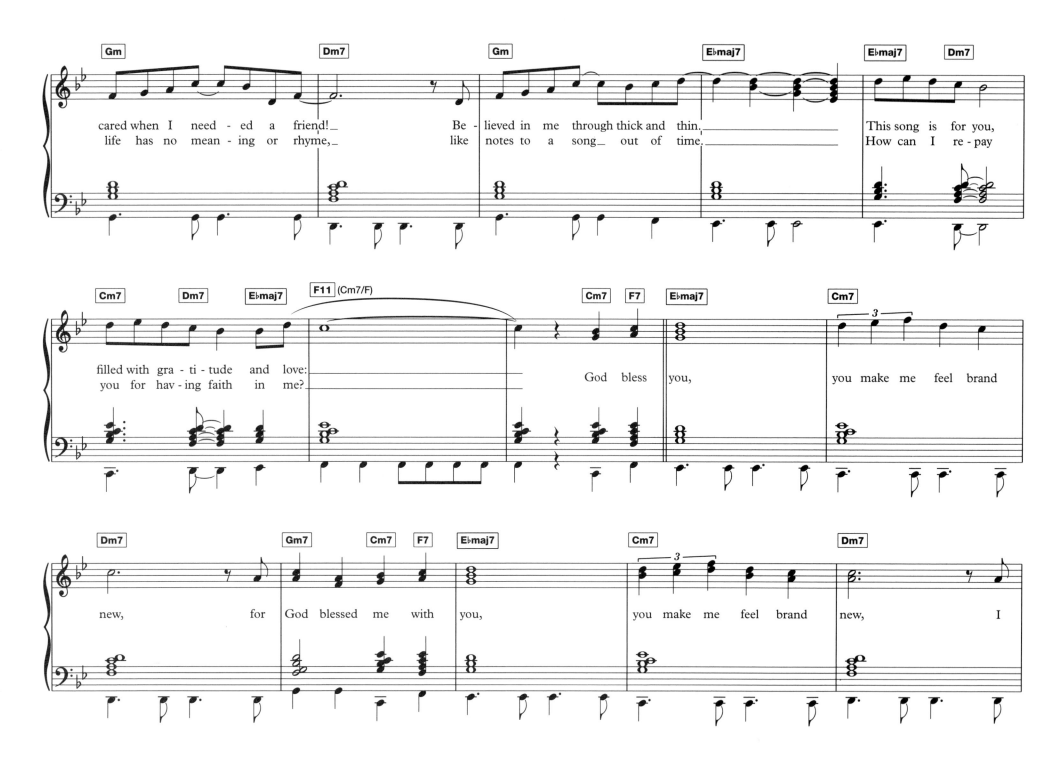

Printed in England
Panda Press · Haverhill · Suffolk · 2/96

also available in this series:

All Time Standards

Bewitched	Moon River
Cheek To Cheek	The Nearness Of You
Crazy Rhythm	Secret Love
I Remember You	September Song
It's Magic	Someone To Watch Over Me
It's Only A Paper Moon	That Old Black Magic
Mona Lisa	When I Fall In Love
You Make Me Feel So Young	

Order Ref: 3509A

Showtunes

Almost Like Being In Love	Getting To Know You
Anything Goes	Hello Dolly!
Bali Ha'i	I've Grown Accustomed To Her Face
Cabaret	My Favorite Things
The Colors Of My Life	Oh, What A Beautiful Mornin'
Consider Yourself	Smoke Gets In Your Eyes
A Foggy Day	They Can't Take That Away From Me
You'll Never Walk Alone	

Order Ref: 3512A

Film Hits

Alfie	I Have Nothing
Arthur's Theme (Best That You Can Do)	(I've Had) The Time Of My Life
Big Spender	La Bamba
Bright Eyes	Raindrops Keep Fallin' On My Head
Endless Love	The Sound Of Music
Evergreen	Star Wars (Main Theme)
For Your Eyes Only	Summer Holiday
Tara's Theme	

Order Ref: 3510A

Easy Listening

Always On My Mind	Laughter In The Rain
Chanson D'Amour	Moonlighting
Earth Angel	Now And Forever
Everybody's Talkin'	The Rose
Goodbye Girl	Trains And Boats And Planes
If I Were A Carpenter	We Don't Cry Out Loud
It's All In The Game	Why Do Fools Fall In Love?
You Make Me Feel Brand New	

Order Ref: 3513A

Love Songs

I Can't Give You Anything But Love	Tenderly
I Just Called To Say I Love You	Three Times A Lady
I'll Be There	Too Marvellous For Words
Killing Me Softly With His Song	Up Where We Belong
Let's Do It (Let's Fall In Love)	The Way You Look Tonight
Love Is A Many-Splendoured Thing	Where Do I Begin? (Love Story)
Love Is Here To Stay	With You I'm Born Again
My Foolish Heart	You Light Up My Life
You'll Never Know	

Order Ref: 3511A

Solid Gold Hits

Don't Let The Sun Go Down On Me	Oh, Pretty Woman
Eternal Flame	The Power Of Love
A Horse With No Name	Save The Best For Last
Hotel California	Solitaire
I Got You Babe	Stand By Me
Nights In White Satin	What A Wonderful World
A Whiter Shade Of Pale	

Order Ref: 3514A